11+
English
Spelling & Vocabulary

Advanced Level
WORKBOOK 11

Stephen C. Curran

with Warren Vokes

Edited by Mark Schofield

This book belongs to

Accelerated Education Publications Ltd.

telegram	**telegraph**	**photograph**
physical	**national**	**cathedral**
principle	**punctual**	**continually**
conversation	**consideration**	**sensation**

Exercise 228a

1) During their __conversation__ he mentioned his brother's boat.

2) There was an old family _____ printed in sepia on the mantelpiece.

3) She had no _____ of returning the ring after he ended their engagement.

4) _____ boys used to ride red motorcycles to deliver the messages.

5) "Solve the anagram and make a well known _____ or saying."

6) They are very Green and, on _____ , always buy recyclable products.

7) The best _____ football teams contest the World Cup every four years.

8) She sings soprano in the church _____ and her husband is a tenor.

9) A _____ of skill and good fortune enabled him to win the final.

10) It was a _____ mistake that cost him dearly.   **Score** [/10]

Exercise 228b

11) "Open the windows please: we need some _____ in here!"

12) He sold his opponent a dummy by managing not to _____ the move.

13) Canterbury _____ is one of the oldest Christian structures in England.

14) Farm animals and pets are known as ' _____ animals'.

15) Some of the players were a little too _____ and the referee warned them.

16) "He is always _____ : you could set your watch by him!"

17) A cross _____ of the community had been asked to complete a questionnaire.

18) The issue under _____ in tonight's programme is truancy.

19) He was _____ interrupting and heckling the speaker.

20) Her revelations on television caused a _____ .   **Score** [/10]

Word Bank

combination
phrase
section
choir

ventilation
fatal
intention
domestic

Word Bank TOTAL 4,560

Across

1. The movement or circulation of fresh air.
3. A picture produced by a camera.
7. A physical feeling caused by having one or more of the sense organs stimulated.
9. Relating to or used in the home or everyday life within a household.
11. A distinct part that can be separated or considered separately from the whole of something.
12. Causing, or capable of causing, death.
13. A message sent by telegraph.
14. A string of words that form a grammatical unit.
16. Existing in the real world and able to be touched and seen.
18. A mixture of different things or factors.
19. An informal talk with somebody.

Down

2. Something that somebody plans to do or achieve.
4. Arriving or taking place at the arranged time.
5. A church that contains a bishop's throne and is the most important church in the bishop's diocese.
6. Happening again and again.

Down (continued)

8. Thoughtful concern for, or sensitivity towards, the feelings of others.
10. A long-distance communication method through wires.
14. An important underlying law or assumption.
15. Relating or belonging to, or representing a nation as a whole.
17. An organized group of singers.

Put the mystery letter (✳) into the box marked **228** below. Add in the mystery letters from puzzles **229** to **234** then rearrange them to make **Dickens's Mystery Word**.

The clue is **COMMUNICATIONS**.

1 ACROSS: VENTILATION

228	229	230	231	232	233	234

Now rearrange them:

Mystery Word:

Score / 20

athletic　　**heroic**　　**majestic**
tropics　　**tenant**　　**vacant**
tyrant　　**elegant**　　**extravagant**
fragrant　　**insurance**　　**assistance**

Across

229

3. A condition that affects what happens or how somebody reacts in a particular situation.
6. Showing great bravery, courage, or determination.
7. An absolute ruler who exercises power cruelly and unjustly.
8. A single thing in a group or collection of things.
14. Experiencing serious lack of contentment or happiness.
15. The parts of the earth between or near the tropics of Cancer and Capricorn.
17. Greatly impressive in appearance.

Across (continued)

18. Somebody who is qualified to fly an aircraft or spacecraft.
19. Help given or made available to another.
20. Possessing a large skeletal structure and having strong muscles.

Down

1. Having a pleasant or sweet smell.
2. Having no occupant or contents.
4. To take hold of an object quickly and firmly.
5. Stylishly graceful, and showing sophistication and good taste in appearance or behaviour.
9. Somebody who rents a building, house, set of rooms, plot of land, or some other piece of property for a fixed period of time.
10. Financial protection against loss or harm.
11. Characterized by spending excessively or wastefully.
12. A small, short-barrelled gun designed to be held in one hand.
13. The act or process of remembering people, things, or events.
16. An excellent or perfect example of something or somebody, or something that is considered a perfect example.

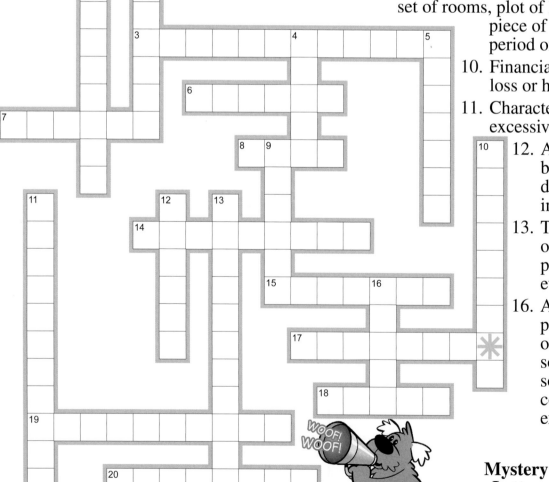

Mystery Letter ▢

Score ▢/20

Exercise 229a

1) She put up a _____ fight against her cancer but finally she succumbed.

2) It is a _____ seascape showing the masts of twenty tall ships under full sail.

3) "Never hesitate: _____ any opportunity and use it to your advantage!"

4) The ship slowed as it neared the coast to take on board a _____ .

5) He lived a _____ existence, struggling from day to day just to survive.

6) Before her holiday in the _____ , she began a course of anti-malaria tablets.

7) He was a _____ and stood trial for his crimes against humanity.

8) She checked her shopping list: there was one _____ that she still had to buy.

9) The fire produced _____ quantities of smoke but very little heat.

10) She drew a small _____ from her handbag and fired it.

Score [/10]

Exercise 229b

11) It was pure _____ that he just happened to be present at the time.

12) She screamed in horror and several people came to her _____ .

13) A service of _____ is held on the Sunday closest to 11th November.

14) His _____ look indicated that he had no idea of the answer to her question.

15) She is an _____ lady, always immaculately dressed and neatly coiffured.

16) He has an _____ build with superb muscle tone and a deep tan.

17) "I recommend that you take out _____ against loss or damage."

18) The _____ asked his landlord to have the storm damage repaired.

19) In an _____ world there would be no war, no fear and no hunger.

20) The lilies have a _____ scent that pervades the room.

Score [/10]

reasonable	capable	probable
probably	despair	despise
description	destruction	energy
convert	concern	convey

Exercise 230a

1) The report stated that the _____ cause of the accident was driver fatigue.

2) "Stay away from him: he's a bad _____ on you."

3) It is an enormous car supermarket selling cars of every _____ .

4) The highest level of _____ is essential to prevent infection.

5) She was called as a _____ for the prosecution at her former employer's trial.

6) The column looked far from vertical when viewed from a different _____ .

7) A fitter came to _____ her appliances from town gas to natural gas.

8) "I'll _____ be there this afternoon but I haven't yet finally decided."

9) The _____ of Hiroshima by an atomic bomb was horrific.

10) The food was _____ but the service was poor.   **Score** | 10 |

Exercise 230b

11) The land is low-lying and _____ to flood when it rains heavily.

12) The sustained period of very cold weather caused an _____ crisis.

13) He called his mother to express his _____ about his father's ill health.

14) What he earned seemed a _____ beside his mountain of debts.

15) His car was always breaking down, so he traded it in for a more _____ one.

16) "Don't _____ . Although it seems hopeless, there's always a solution."

17) "The Union has _____ and can protect its members from exploitation."

18) His actions were well-meant but _____ of being misinterpreted.

19) Newspapers _____ politicians who abuse their power and position.

20) A new pipeline was built to _____ crude oil to the refinery. **Score** | 10 |

6

Word Bank TOTAL 4,600

Across — 230

2. As is likely or to be expected.
5. A profound feeling that there is no hope.
6. The act or process of destroying something.
9. A reason to worry, or something that causes worry.
11. To change the nature or form of something, or to be changed in nature or form.
14. The degree to which somebody keeps clean or a place is kept clean.
16. Likely to experience or do something, often something unpleasant or hazardous.
17. Something that has little or no importance, significance, or value.
18. The effect of something on a person, thing, or event.

Down

1. Likely to exist, occur, or be true, although evidence is insufficient to prove or predict it.
3. A figure formed by two lines diverging from a common point.
4. To look down on and feel contempt for somebody or something.
7. Somebody who saw or heard something that happened and gives evidence about it.
8. Sensible and capable of making rational judgments.
9. To take somebody or something somewhere.
10. A written or verbal account, representation, or explanation of something.
12. Able to be trusted to do what is expected or has been promised.
13. A tissue that is specialized to undergo repeated contraction and relaxation, thereby producing movement of body parts.
14. Good at a particular task or job or a number of different things.
15. Liveliness and forcefulness.

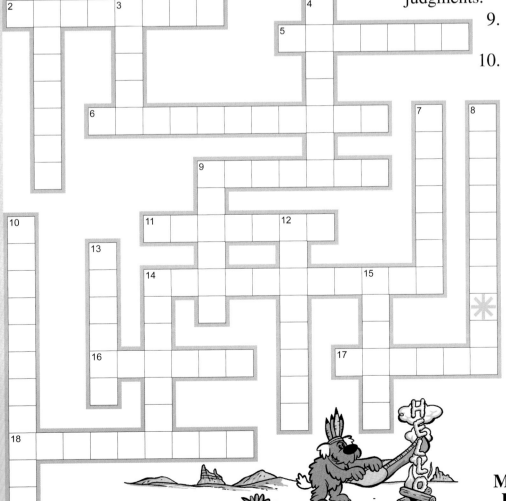

Mystery Letter

Score / 20

presence **evidence** **residence**
reference **famine** **medicine**
genuine **granite** **definite**
reception **ambition** **satisfaction**

Across

231

5. A feeling or expression of opposition.
6. Teaching in a particular subject or skill, or the facts or skills taught.
9. A drug or remedy used for treating illness, especially in liquid form.
11. The receiving of something given or sent.
12. Something that gives a sign or proof of the existence or truth of something, or that helps somebody to come to a particular decision.
13. An action prohibited by law.
16. Having the qualities or value claimed.
18. A period during which somebody is away.
19. A strong feeling of wanting to be successful in life and achieve great things.
20. The process of mentioning or alluding to somebody or something.

Down

1. A severe shortage of food resulting in widespread hunger.
2. The house, flat, or other dwelling in which somebody lives.
3. A group of travelling entertainers, including clowns, acrobats and sometimes animal trainers and their animals.
4. The feeling of pleasure that comes when a need or desire is fulfilled.
7. To formally signal respect to another member of the armed forces or to a flag.
8. Precise and distinct in describing the limits of something.
10. Something done or a way of behaving that is not genuine but is meant to deceive other people.
14. A coarse-grained igneous rock made up of feldspar, mica, and at least 20 per cent quartz.
15. The physical existence of somebody or something in a particular place.
17. An official who supervises play and enforces the rules of the game in some sports.

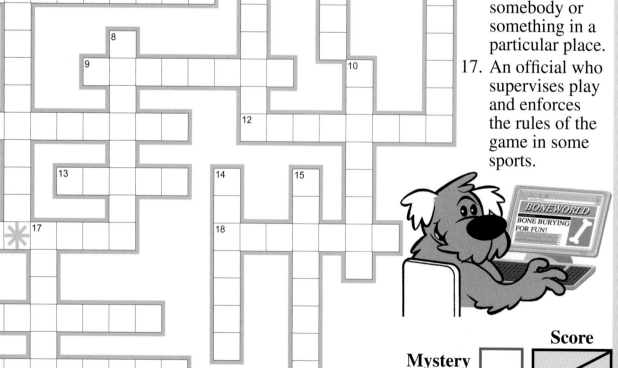

Mystery Letter

Score

/20

objection   instruction
absence   pretence
umpire   crime
circus   salute

Word Bank
TOTAL
4,620

Exercise 231a

1) The statue of Eros, the god of love, stands in Piccadilly _____ .

2) After an _____ of over five years, the band had a record in the charts.

3) "I might be able to go too: I'll give you a _____ answer tomorrow."

4) Her _____ is to become a leading gynaecologist in a teaching hospital.

5) He seemed an affable and _____ person who would fit in well with the others.

6) The UN peace-keeping troops maintained a heavy _____ in the city.

7) The town was gripped in a _____ wave with a significant increase in burglaries.

8) She located the directory in the _____ section of the local library.

9) He could no longer keep up the _____ and admitted that he had lied.

10) The _____ overruled the linesman and called the ball 'out'. **Score** / 10

Exercise 231b

11) He received a written _____ to rent the property for his client.

12) Mormon pioneers quarried massive _____ blocks to build the Salt Lake Temple.

13) She had no _____ in principle but doubted the wisdom of the proposal.

14) The signal is weak and _____ is poor on this television channel.

15) The archeologists sifted the soil for _____ of Roman remains.

16) The new recruit failed to _____ the officer and was rebuked by the sergeant.

17) 'Chequers' is the official country _____ of the serving Prime Minister.

18) He chose a career in _____ to enable him to care for sick people.

19) The _____ is widespread and many could die before aid arrives.

20) The mystery was never explained to my _____ . **Score** / 10

ae © 2006 Stephen Curran   9

distribute	gratitude	destitute
volume	detail	deposit
develop	strength	strengthen
acquire	acquaint	acquainted

Exercise 232a

1) "I'm sorry to _____ you, but I shan't be joining you on the trip."

2) The river was _____ after the heavy rain and likely to burst its banks.

3) The monks of the _____ made mead from honey to sell to the public.

4) The barrister was keen to _____ the jury with the facts surrounding the case.

5) It is an exact replica with all the intricate _____ faithfully reproduced.

6) Jesus was able to _____ five fishes and two loaves among 5,000 people.

7) The _____ of proof always rests with the prosecution in a trial.

8) He is an old _____ whom she has not met since their school days.

9) Elizabeth I finally decided to _____ her cousin, Mary, Queen of Scots.

10) The tensile _____ of cast iron is negligible.

Score 10

Exercise 232b

11) They expressed their _____ to the staff by making a donation to the hospice.

12) She was not well _____ with her husband's side of the family.

13) He placed the film into the tray of chemicals and watched it slowly _____ .

14) She left a _____ and returned later to collect and pay for the bracelet.

15) The families were _____ and dependent on charity.

16) She spent many years studying the migration _____ of swallows.

17) He made his fortune as an entrepreneur and now lives a life of _____ .

18) Countless failures served only to _____ his resolve to succeed one day.

19) She lived in France for a year to _____ fluency in the language.

20) "I can't hear. Turn up the _____ please."

Score 10

Word Bank
acquaintance luxury swollen abbey disappoint burden execute pattern

Word Bank TOTAL 4,640

Across

232

3. The physical power to carry out demanding tasks.
4. To get or obtain possession of something.
5. Made larger, fuller or rounder, or expanded in size or shape.
9. A feeling of being thankful to somebody for doing something.
11. To deliver or share things out to people.
12. To put an instruction or plan into effect.
14. A repeated decorative design, for example on fabric.
16. To make somebody, or yourself, aware of or familiar with something.
17. An individual separable part of something, especially one of several items of information.

Across (continued)

18. To be less good, attractive, or satisfactory than was hoped or expected.
19. The size of a three-dimensional space enclosed within, or occupied by, an object.

Down

1. To put or drop something somewhere.
2. Somebody who is known slightly rather than intimately.
6. An activity that gives great pleasure, especially one only rarely indulged in.
7. To change, or cause to change, and become larger, stronger, or more impressive, successful, or advanced.
8. To make something stronger or more powerful, or increase in strength or force.
10. Having some, often not very much, knowledge of something.
11. Lacking all money, resources and possessions necessary for subsistence.
13. A building or buildings occupied by monks under an abbot or nuns under an abbess.
15. A load being carried.

Mystery Letter

Score 20

11

Across

233

2. A formal and usually written request for something.
4. To plan and make something in a skilful or artistic way.
5. To redirect something that strikes a surface, especially light, heat, or sound.
7. An identifiable or distinctive quality of food or drink perceived with the combined senses of taste and smell.
10. To hurt somebody's feelings, or cause resentment, irritation, anger, or displeasure.
12. Somebody who is on a journey to a particular place or who uses a particular form of transport.
13. To set free a person or animal who is imprisoned, trapped, or confined in some way.
14. Something said or written in reply to a statement or question from somebody else.
17. To give up a paid or unpaid post voluntarily.
18. The part of something that is left after other parts have gone or been used up.
19. To be against something or to take an active stance against something.

Down

1. To have a favourable opinion of somebody or something.
3. Somebody who carries a message or messages between people.
6. To invite somebody to participate in a fight, contest or competition.

Down (continued)

8. An actively hostile attitude towards something, or a resistant stance against something.
9. To keep something back for future use or for some specific purpose.
10. To subject a person or a people to a harsh or cruel form of domination.
11. An institution of higher or further education.
15. On the side that faces something, or at the furthest distance possible from something.
16. To disclose something that was unknown or secret.

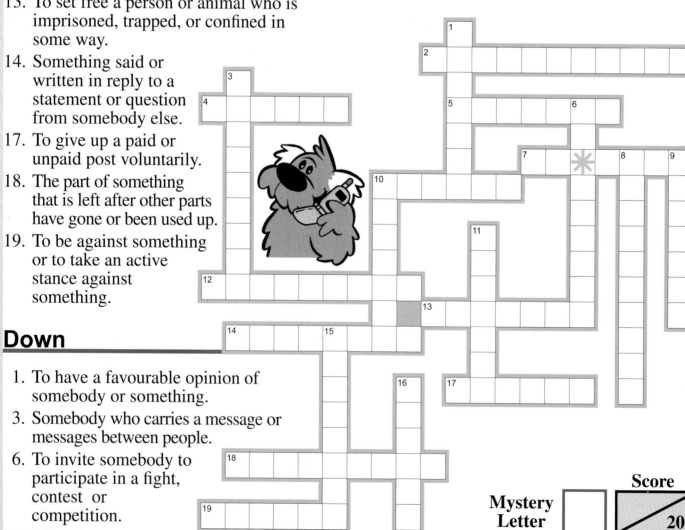

Mystery Letter

Score

20

Exercise 233a

1) She completed and returned the job _____ form.

2) The car salesman removed the cover to _____ the latest model.

3) Her parents _____ of her decision to apply for a place at university.

4) The anti-vivisection group would not state openly that they _____ violence.

5) He is a seasoned _____ who has visited over fifteen countries.

6) The _____ of Cardinals sat to deliberate and elect a new Pope.

7) Public _____ to the proposed development was growing.

8) The sailor threw the _____ line to the dock worker on the quay.

9) Many of the members _____ against the club's strict dress code.

10) She waited for a _____ but he remained silent.   **Score** / 10

Exercise 233b

11) It has an unusual _____ , rather like aniseed with a hint of mint.

12) The elegant _____ of the wings and body gave *Concorde* a graceful appearance.

13) "I think you should sit there quietly and _____ on your misconduct."

14) He took out the £1 coins and put the _____ of his change in a jar.

15) The foreman handed over to his _____ number on the next shift.

16) The company's public relations manager handed a press _____ to the journalists.

17) The conquering army implemented a harsh regime to _____ the population.

18) The sentry shouted out a _____ : "Halt! Who goes there? Friend or foe?"

19) The winning cyclist kept something in _____ for the sprint finish.

20) He refuses to _____ even though his position is untenable. **Score** / 10

vapour	**rumour**	**occasion**
occasionally	**generous**	**numerous**
enormous	**mischievous**	**marvellous**
innocent	**independent**	**excitement**

Exercise 234a

1) He replied to the _____ in the newspaper and bought the item.

2) She visited her mother every Saturday and _____ during the week too.

3) He suffers from emphysema and has been an _____ for many years.

4) Her insurance company required an _____ assessment of the damage.

5) The steam pipe had fractured and a cloud of water _____ filled the room.

6) He decided to _____ control of the company to his daughter and retire.

7) An _____ crowd waited outside the palace to cheer the royal couple.

8) She used a fork to _____ the pastry before placing the pie in the oven.

9) The waitress poured a _____ amount of cream onto the gateau.

10) "You must _____ playing the piano every day."   **Score** ☐ 10

Exercise 234b

11) It began as a _____ but by lunchtime everyone believed it to be the truth.

12) The children found it hard to contain their _____ as Christmas drew near.

13) One child in the class was _____ and showed no regard for the teacher.

14) He passed an _____ remark but she misunderstood and turned on him.

15) He is a _____ child, always playing pranks and teasing people.

16) She raised her hand to _____ her eyes from the sun's glare.

17) He tried without success on _____ occasions to beat his sister at tennis.

18) It was _____ to see his family again after living abroad for five years.

19) "Don't _____ that the house is empty by forgetting to cancel the milk."

20) He carries a compass but never has _____ to use it.   **Score** ☐ 10

14   © 2006 Stephen Curran

Across

234

3. Showing a lack of respect and excessive boldness.
6. To penetrate through or into something with a sharp pointed object.
8. To publicize the qualities of a product, service, business, or event.
10. A gaseous substance.
13. Extraordinarily wonderful.
14. Not guilty of a crime or offence.
15. Free from authority, control, or domination.
16. Having or showing a willingness to give money, help, or time freely.
19. Behaving, or likely to behave, in a naughty or troublesome way, but in fun and not meaning serious harm.
20. Not acceptable or correct because of being based on a mistake or employing flawed reasoning.

Down

1. The amount of something, especially a crop, produced by cultivation or labour.
2. Many in number.
4. The feeling or condition of lively enjoyment or pleasant anticipation.
5. Now and then.
7. The act of advertising something.
9. Unusually large or great in size, amount, or degree.
11. To do something repeatedly in order to improve performance.
12. A particular time.
17. A piece of armour carried on the arm.
18. A generally circulated story, report, or statement without facts to confirm its truth.

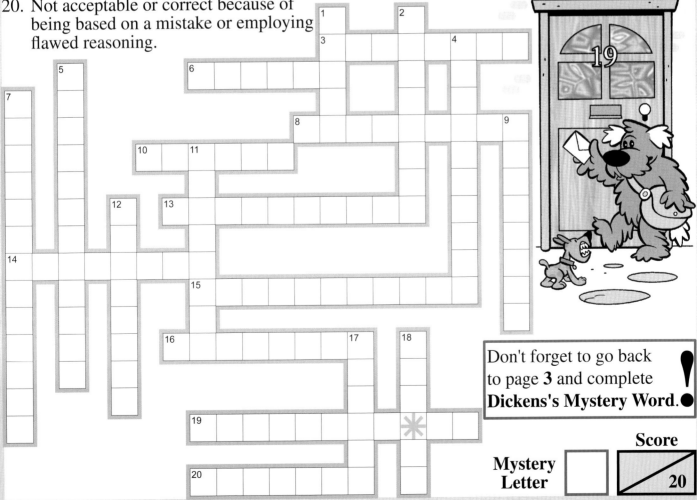

Don't forget to go back to page **3** and complete **Dickens's Mystery Word.**

Mystery Letter ☐

Score / 20

© 2006 Stephen Curran

15

At the Birthday Party

Can you find all these words in the picture below? Write the correct word against each number. When you have finished you can colour in the picture if you want to.

candles	**entertainer**	**card**	**doll**	**balloons**
slice	**presents**	**jelly**	**patch**	**blindfold**
donkey	**lemonade**	**fairy cake**	**zip fastener**	**éclair**

1._____ 2._____ 3._____

4._____ 5._____ 6._____

7._____ 8._____ 9._____

10._____ 11._____ 12._____

13._____ 14._____ 15._____

On the Canal

Can you find all these words in the picture below? Write the correct word against each number.

painter	lifebelt	landing net	lock	narrowboat
duck	railing	fender	hamper	bait
fishing rod	lock keeper	stern	reel	bow

1._____ 2._____ 3._____

4._____ 5._____ 6._____

7._____ 8._____ 9._____

10._____ 11._____ 12._____

13._____ 14._____ 15._____

invention   **patient**   **impatient**

impatience   **digest**   **digestion**

soul   **mould**   **poultry**

provoke   **proclaim**   **pronounce**

Across

235

3. The view somebody takes about a certain issue.
6. To make somebody feel angry or exasperated.
9. A container that gives a shape to a molten or liquid substance poured into it to harden.
11. Eagerness to do something immediately.
14. Having advanced cultural and social development.
15. To articulate sounds or words.
16. With a very cold temperature.
18. The controlling of something or the managing of the way it works.

Down

1. The innermost being or nature of somebody.
2. The ability to process food in the body.
4. Annoyed by being kept waiting.
5. To announce something publicly or formally.
7. To pledge devotion or dedication to somebody or something.
8. A thing that somebody has created, especially a device or process.
10. To think about something and come to understand or appreciate what it means.

Down (continued)

12. To go on to do something.
13. Somebody who is being given medical treatment.
14. Polite, but in a way that is cold and formal.
15. Domestic fowl in general raised for meat or eggs.
17. Somebody who is the legal inheritor of something.

Put the mystery letter (✳) into the box marked **235** below. Add in the mystery letters from puzzles **236** to **242** then rearrange them to make **Oliver's Mystery Word**. The clue is **CLOTHING**.

235	236	237	238	239	240	241	242

Now rearrange them:

Mystery Word:

Score

/20

proceed **opinion**
frigid   **civil**
civilized **operation**
heir   **commit**

Word Bank
TOTAL
4,700

Exercise 235a

1) His story is pure _____ and bears little or no relation to the truth.

2) Our generation is the unfortunate _____ to decades of pollution.

3) Her childhood experience helped _____ her personality.

4) He received a very _____ reception and wished he had not come.

5) She used the opportunity to _____ her innocence before she was imprisoned.

6) The Dunkirk evacuation in 1940 was a huge military and naval _____ .

7) He is a _____ man: exceedingly slow to anger and tolerant to a fault.

8) She used her frailty to _____ sympathy from her captors.

9) The police did not prosecute the culprit, so the victims began a _____ action.

10) "All his _____ is free range: he detests battery farming." **Score** / 10

Exercise 235b

11) He extracted the salient points from the paper and presented them in a _____ .

12) He could no longer contain his _____ : he had to *do* something.

13) "I now _____ you man and wife," proclaimed the registrar.

14) She acted in a _____ way, showing the utmost courtesy and respect.

15) The crowd cheered as they watched the parade _____ along the route.

16) The electorate were _____ for change and voted in a new government.

17) He is able to _____ intricate details to memory and recall them perfectly.

18) The doctor referred his patient to a specialist for a second _____ .

19) "Stress is bad for your _____ : it causes stomach ulcers."

20) It is dull, repetitive, _____ -destroying work. **Score** / 10

commence	recommend	recollect
shipping	comrade	complaint
humour	endeavour	tobacco
pension	provision	decision

Exercise 236a

1) Sir Walter Raleigh introduced _____ to England in the 16th Century.

2) She went to the doctor with a _____ and he prescribed her medication.

3) The Prime Minister asked the Queen to _____ parliament.

4) Advances in forensic science have enabled police to _____ more crimes.

5) She married a _____ magnate whose company owned a huge fleet.

6) His team finished top of their _____ and won promotion.

7) Attempting the climb was a heroic _____ but he failed to reach the summit.

8) "If you continue to _____ me with that whistle, I'll take it away from you!"

9) The _____ to turn back, due to the bad weather, proved to be right.

10) Many families in poorer regions still live in _____ .   **Score** | 10

Exercise 236b

11) Ill-health forced her to retire from work and to claim a disability _____ .

12) The film has little to _____ it other than its special effects.

13) "Can you _____ what your daughter was wearing?"

14) The constant sound of barking dogs _____ him intensely.

15) The enquiry into the incident found that he alone was _____ responsible.

16) The young recruit was proud that the older soldiers regarded him as a _____ .

17) At the _____ of their negotiations, both parties signed the agreement.

18) "I know he can be demanding but just _____ him to keep the peace."

19) The performance is scheduled to _____ at 8.30 pm.

20) No _____ has been made for non-ambulant visitors.   **Score** | 10

conclusion **division**
solve **dissolve**
wholly **annoy**
annoyed **poverty**

Across

236

1. The act of supplying or providing something.
4. Harassed or bothered somebody repeatedly.
9. A statement expressing dissatisfaction with something.
11. To begin happening or to begin something.
12. Somebody who is either a close friend or a companion.
13. Totally and in every way or to the fullest extent.
14. To become absorbed in a liquid solution, or cause this process to occur to a solid.
16. The act or business of transporting goods.
18. To make an effort to achieve something.

Across (continued)

19. To find a way of dealing successfully with a problem or difficulty.
20. A decision made or an opinion formed after considering the relevant facts or evidence.

Down

2. To bring something back to mind.
3. To suggest something as worthy of being accepted, used, or done.
5. The quality or content of something that elicits amusement and laughter.
6. A plant whose large leaves are dried and processed primarily for smoking.
7. To make somebody feel impatient or angry.
8. The state of not having enough money to take care of basic needs.
10. Something that somebody chooses or makes up his or her mind about, after considering it and other possible choices.
15. The act of separating or splitting something into parts, or an instance of this.
17. A fixed amount of money paid regularly to somebody during retirement.

Mystery Letter [ ]

Score [/ 20]

mutiny · variety · society
sacrifice · margin · origin
original · moral · crystal
transform · translate · character

Across

237

5. A clear, colourless mineral, especially quartz.
6. Existing first, from the beginning, or before other people or things.
9. To change people or things completely.
10. To bring somebody or something into existence.
11. Delicate and pretty.
12. The largest of the three sovereign nations that make up the Iberian peninsula.

Across (continued)

13. To satisfy a thirst by drinking something.
15. The reaching of a place after coming from another place.
16. With a charming, old-fashioned quality.
18. A starting point or first cause.
19. The set of qualities that make somebody or something distinctive.

Down

1. A plan of action.
2. To give an equivalent in another language for a particular word or phrase.
3. A blank space on the left or right edge, or at the top or bottom, of a written or printed page.
4. A rebellion against legal authority.
7. A snack or light meal, usually made with two slices of bread with a filling in between.
8. A structured community of people bound together by similar traditions, institutions, or nationality.
12. A symbolic offering made to a god.
14. The quality of being varied or diversified.
17. A conclusion about how to behave or proceed drawn from a story or event.

Score

Mystery Letter | 20

Exercise 237a

1) Work began to _____ the wasteland into a children's playground.

2) The firemen played water from their hoses onto the blaze to _____ the flames.

3) He had to act quickly: travelling at that speed left no _____ for error.

4) The _____ course provided a perfect balance between work and study.

5) The _____ on HMVA *Bounty* in 1789 was led by Fletcher Christian.

6) ETA, a terrorist group in _____ , is attempting to achieve Basque independence.

7) The staff quickly became bored due to the lack of _____ in their work.

8) "He is a _____ old man whose dress, speech and manners are from the 1940s!"

9) She studied the cast list in the _____ before the play began.

10) The _____ drawings were lost but exact copies still exist.   **Score** / 10

Exercise 237b

11) Hydraulics _____ the pressure of a finger into powerful movement.

12) She wore a _____ pair of slippers trimmed with lace.

13) "After days of heated discussions their _____ at an agreement seems unlikely."

14) He played Malvolio, the pompous _____ , in Shakespeare's *Twelfth Night*.

15) The rights of women in modern _____ have been supported by legislation.

16) He proposed that the committee _____ a new category of 'life member'.

17) She had to _____ her rook to his queen to enable her to gain the advantage.

18) He looked on the internet for the _____ of the idiom *"as pleased as Punch"*.

19) The fortune teller peered into her _____ ball to predict the future.

20) They won a _____ victory but were not awarded damages.   **Score** / 10

creation   **emigrate**   **emigrant**
obstinate   **suitable**   **creditable**
honourable   **peaceable**   **manageable**
Chinese   **interfere**   **supreme**

Exercise 238a

1) Many young people decide to _____ and seek their fortune abroad.

2) She cut up the food to make it more _____ for her young son.

3) The wind blew in from the northeast making it feel _____ cold.

4) She played a _____ rendition of Christian Sinding's *Rustle of Spring*.

5) The riders tried to catch and overtake each other in the cycling _____ .

6) He arrived at an _____ solution by applying his mind to the problem.

7) Paper making, the compass, gunpowder and printing are all _____ inventions.

8) St. Paul's Cathedral is the _____ example of Sir Christopher Wren's skill.

9) An _____ blockage in the waste pipe resisted all attempts to clear it.

10) He lacked _____ footwear for the muddy conditions.   **Score**   **10**

Exercise 238b

11) Although happily married, she continued to _____ the loss of her independence.

12) Switzerland, since declaring itself neutral, has remained a _____ country.

13) Prohibition was an _____ measure enforced by the 18th Amendment in 1920.

14) He left his well-paid job to _____ his ambition to care for the homeless overseas.

15) The company introduced a training _____ to improve productivity.

16) The hat she wore at Ascot was an amazing _____ that turned people's heads.

17) "Trust the British weather to _____ with our plans for a trip to the seaside!"

18) At the end of his service, he left the army with an _____ discharge.

19) He was a British _____ who had moved to Australia in the 1950s.

20) She found a reliable _____ who confirmed the rumour.   **Score**   **10**

extreme	extremely
scheme	pursue
pursuit	mourn
source	intelligent

Word Bank
TOTAL
4,760

Across

(238)

1. Inclined towards peace and avoiding contentious situations.
5. The bringing of something into existence.
6. The place where something begins.
7. Able to be handled or controlled without much difficulty.
10. Above all others in power, authority, rank, status, or skill.
14. Somebody who leaves a place to go and live in another country.
15. To meddle in the affairs of other people.
17. Determined not to agree to other people's wishes or accept their suggestions.
18. A group of related languages spoken across most of China.
19. To follow or chase somebody in order to catch, overtake, or attack him or her.

Down

2. To a very high degree.
3. Having intelligence, especially to a highly developed degree.
4. To feel and show sadness because somebody has died.
8. To leave a place, especially a native country, to go and live in another country.
9. Bringing credit or worthy of praise.
10. A secret and cunning plan, especially one designed to cause damage or harm.
11. The effort made to try to achieve or obtain something over a period of time.
12. Guided by, or with a reputation for having, strong moral and ethical principles.
13. Of the right type or quality for a particular purpose.
16. Highest in intensity or degree.

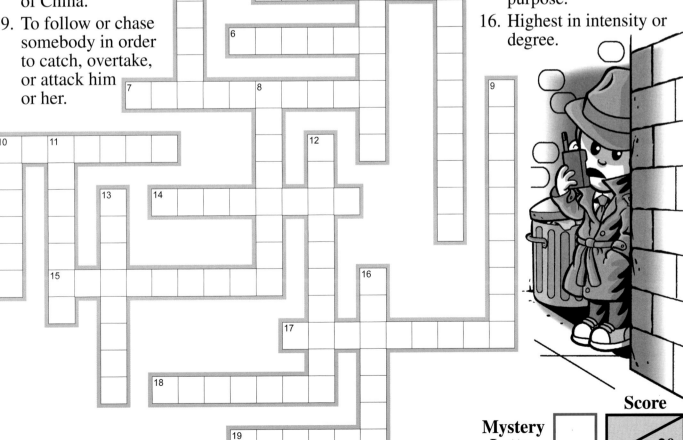

Mystery Letter

Score

20

ae © 2006 Stephen Curran

25

Oliver's
Page of Knowledge
Inventors and Inventions

Trevor Bayliss ⑦
Clue: This man's invention is powered by a constant velocity spring. It enables people who have no access to mains supply electricity or replacement batteries to keep in touch with news and world events.

John Logie Baird ⑩
Clue: He was born in Helensburgh, Argyle, Scotland in 1888. The first public demonstration of his invention of image transmission was in the Selfridge's department store in London in 1926.

Rudolph Diesel ⑨
Clue: In 1892, he invented a propulsion system in which the fuel is ignited by being suddenly exposed to the high temperature and pressure of a compressed gas. He intended to use a variety of fuels including coal dust.

Laszio Biro ②
Clue: He was a Hungarian journalist who, after noticing that the ink used in printing newspapers dried quickly, invented in 1938 this revolutionary writing implement.

Charles Babbage ③
Clue: He was the first to conceptualize and design a fully programmable version as early as 1820, but the device was never actually constructed in his lifetime.

Inventor		Invention
1. _____	invented	_____
2. _____	invented	_____
3. _____	invented	_____
4. _____	invented	_____
5. _____	invented	_____

Safety Match · Jet Engine Television · Clockwork Radio Ballpoint Pen · Diesel Engine Pneumatic Tyre · Plough Computer · Spinning Jenny

"Link the name of the inventor with their invention in the answers below."

Gustaf Erik Pasch ④
Clue: In 1844, this Swede invented a safer version of an earlier invention of 1836. His invention used red instead of white phosphorous and separated the combustible ingredients until the product was used.

Robert William Thomson ⑧
Clue: In 1845, this Scotsman patented the Aerial Wheel. His invention was only applied to horse-drawn carriages but was later re-invented to be used on bicycles.

Frank Whittle ⑤
Clue: On 16th January 1930, in England, he submitted patents for his own design of a device that now powers aircraft all over the world. It was granted in 1932.

Joseph Foljambe ①
Clue: He developed the first commercially successful version of this implement in 1730. It was made from iron with a mouldboard that would cut, lift and turn over the strip of earth.

James Hargreaves ⑥
Clue: In about 1764 his invention revolutionised the cotton trade. His device dramatically reduced the amount of work needed to produce yarn, with a single worker able to work eight or more spools at once.

Inventor   Invention

6. _____ invented _____

7. _____ invented _____

8. _____ invented _____

9. _____ invented _____

10. _____ invented _____

intelligence	difference	offence
apparent	judgment	parliament
incident	magnificent	compliment
thorough	sustain	maintain

Exercise 239a

1) The rules state that the panel's _____ is final.

2) From the top of the hill on a cloudless day the view is _____ .

3) The grey _____ was introduced into England and South Africa from America.

4) The _____ has been superseded by the computer and word processing.

5) The survey revealed that the floor could not _____ the weight of the machine.

6) Governments around the world gather _____ about each other.

7) The hunter tracked his _____ for several miles before sighting it.

8) He sent an email to _____ her on passing her driving test.

9) _____ debated the bill in an all-night sitting and rose at 5.30am.

10) "I still _____ that he knew that the notes were forged." **Score** [/ 10]

Exercise 239b

11) The guttering had fractured and a _____ of rainwater cascaded down the wall.

12) Their homework was to write an _____ entitled *The Merits of Mediocrity*.

13) His calmness and _____ indifference to the situation surprised his parents.

14) The decor is _____ and ostentatious with overuse of gilt and garish colours.

15) The Cuban missile crisis in 1962 was a major international _____ .

16) The *Mona Lisa* is arguably the most famous _____ in Western art history.

17) His off the cuff remarks caused great _____ and he apologized unreservedly.

18) He dictated an important letter for his secretary to _____ and post immediately.

19) They had a _____ of opinion but soon resolved it amicably.

20) The doctor gave her a _____ examination. **Score** [/ 10]

28

ae

Word Bank

portrait   quarry
torrent   squirrel
essay   type
typewriter   vulgar

Word Bank TOTAL 4,780

Across

1. The intellectual skill or knowledge of somebody.
3. The quality of being different from or unlike something or somebody else.
5. The decision arrived at and pronounced by a court of law.
9. Extremely careful and accurate in doing something.
11. A short piece of written work set as an assignment for a student.
14. To make a situation or course of action continue in the same way as before.
16. Something said to express praise and approval.
18. Clearly seen or understood.
19. An electrical or mechanical device for printing words on individual sheets of paper.

Across (continued)

20. A category of things or people whose members share some qualities.

Down

2. A fast and powerful rush of liquid, especially water.
4. Crude or obscene.
6. Beautiful, impressive, and splendid in appearance.
7. A painting, photograph or drawing of somebody, somebody's face, or a related group.
8. A nation's legislative body, made up of elected and sometimes non-elected representatives.
10. An official crime, or a crime against moral, social, or other accepted standards.
12. A small, bushy-tailed rodent that lives in trees and eats nuts and seeds.
13. Something that happens, especially a single event.
15. To manage to withstand something and continue doing something in spite of it.
17. An open excavation from which stone or other material is extracted by blasting, cutting, or drilling.

Mystery Letter

Score
/20

guarantee	accommodation	destination
freight	isles	angling
chisel	hand-grenade	evaporate
authoress	ellipse	hazardous

Across

240

1. A European songbird that lays its eggs in the nests of other birds.
5. A female writer of a book or other text.
8. Extremely tired or weak.
10. A tool for cutting and shaping wood or stone.
12. Consistently trustworthy and loyal, especially to a person, a promise, or duty.
14. A shape like a stretched circle with slightly longer, flatter sides.
17. The sport of catching fish with a hook, line and rod.
18. Goods or cargo carried by a commercial means of transport.
19. A room or building to live in.

Across (continued)

20. A game similar to tennis using rackets to strike a shuttlecock back and forth across a high net.

Down

2. Caused by a lack of courage, or lacking courage.
3. A small bomb designed to be thrown by hand and detonated by a time fuse.
4. Potentially dangerous to human beings or the environment.
6. To damage somebody's dignity or pride, especially publicly.
7. Islands, often small ones.
9. Cutting and preparing boneless portions of fish, poultry or meat.
11. To change liquid into a vapour.
13. The place to which somebody or something is going or must go.
15. Something that assures a particular outcome.
16. Socks, stockings and tights, considered collectively.

Mystery Letter

Score

20

© 2006 Stephen Curran

exhausted
cowardly
faithful
filleting

badminton
hosiery
humiliate
cuckoo

Word Bank
TOTAL
4,800

Exercise 240a

1) The mine is fully worked out and the coal seams are _____ .

2) He was _____ his presentation towards a more mature audience.

3) With their _____ only a few kilometres further on, their pace quickened.

4) The Mills bomb was the first modern fragmentation _____ .

5) She took her _____ racket to the sports shop to have it restrung.

6) She is a successful _____ but writes under a male nom de plume.

7) The sculptor studied his maquette and began to _____ the stone.

8) A rugby ball is shaped like an _____ to make it easier to carry and handle.

9) The _____ of Scilly form an archipelago of islands off the Cornish coast.

10) The waiter stood by their table _____ the Dover sole.

Score [/ 10]

Exercise 240b

11) The mist slowly began to _____ once the sun broke through.

12) The journalist submitted a _____ account of the events to his editor.

13) They heard the two-note call of the _____ from deep within the woods.

14) She bought two pairs of socks and four pairs of tights in the _____ department.

15) He could not _____ them seats for tomorrow afternoon's flight.

16) She rang the Post Office to set up an _____ address.

17) A chemical spillage can be extremely _____ to the fire brigade.

18) He asked if the company could _____ the parts by air in order to save time.

19) Robbing the old lady was a _____ and despicable act.

20) She would _____ him by ridiculing him in public.

Score [/ 10]

coconut	chess	hula-hula
assassinate	collie	emergency
ladle	fanatical	tennis
obliging	rallies	beverages

Exercise 241a

1) A vending machine dispenses coffee and other hot _____ .

2) The _____ is the headquarters of the United States Department of Defense.

3) The ballet class learnt how to _____ on one foot with their arms held aloft.

4) At the end of the evening the _____ shared out their tips.

5) The tourists were entertained by _____ dancers wearing grass skirts.

6) Visitors to Britain are often surprised to find our policemen so _____ .

7) The Royal _____ , Greenwich was commissioned in 1675.

8) A gypsy dancer shook her _____ and struck it with her hand.

9) He was fined and had his licence endorsed for _____ the speed limit.

10) The women had _____ all day and were extremely tired.   **Score** [/10]

Exercise 241b

11) The workhouse master used a _____ to serve gruel from the copper to Oliver Twist.

12) His father had a shy and managed to knock off and win a _____ .

13) The club's supporters are _____ about their football team and hate to lose.

14) "When the stock market _____ I'll consider selling some of my shares."

15) Real _____ is the original racket sport from which the modern game originates.

16) _____ is played on a square board of eight rows (ranks) and eight columns (files).

17) The Opposition tried to _____ the Government Minister's reputation.

18) The pilot was forced to make an _____ landing when an engine failed.

19) The internal angle at each vertex of a regular _____ is 135°.

20) He trained the Border _____ to be an excellent sheepdog.   **Score** [/10]

Across

(241)

1. A game played on a chequered board by two players, each with 16 pieces representing a king and his attendants.
7. A spoon with a long handle and a deep bowl.
8. Recovers or improves after a setback, crisis, or period of illness, inactivity, or deterioration.
11. A fruit consisting of a hard fibrous husk surrounding a single-seeded nut with a firm white flesh and hollow core containing sweet-tasting liquid.
13. A fast complete spin of the body.
16. An unexpected and sudden event that must be dealt with urgently.
17. A shallow, single-handed drum with jingling metallic discs in its frame.

Across (continued)

18. Worked long and hard.
19. A geometrical figure that has five sides and five angles.

Down

1. A dog with a long narrow muzzle, originally bred to herd sheep.
2. To kill somebody, especially a political leader or other public figure, by a sudden violent attack.
3. Going beyond the limits of something in quantity, degree, or scope.
4. A Polynesian or Hawaiian dance.
5. Excessively enthusiastic about a particular belief, cause, or activity.
6. A building, station, or artificial satellite used for scientific observation of natural phenomena.
9. A game played on a rectangular court by two, or two pairs of, players with rackets who hit a ball back and forth over a net.
10. Women who bring food or drink to tables.
12. Drinks other than water.
14. Willing to be helpful or do favours.
15. A closed plane figure that has eight sides and eight angles.

Mystery Letter

Score / 20

33

plateau	tripod	prompter
skyscraper	tourist	piecemeal
wig	symmetrical	poncho
triangle	proteins	unaffected

Exercise 242a

1) After all the _____ , the opening night had finally arrived.

2) The bed-sit was equipped with a small _____ in one corner.

3) The taller the _____ , the more prestigious the company.

4) He supplied his publisher _____ with chapters of his novel.

5) She stood in the wings acting as _____ for the actors on stage.

6) Ships and planes have mysteriously disappeared inside the Bermuda _____ .

7) At the end of extra time it was a draw, so the match was decided on _____ .

8) Her house was just above the high water line and was _____ by the flood.

9) The powdered _____ remains part of the official attire of an English barrister.

10) She replaced the toner _____ in the laser printer.   **Score** | 10

Exercise 242b

11) Nowadays, a waterproof _____ is a standard in military field uniforms.

12) His astrological telescope is mounted on a _____ for stability.

13) Professional golfers employ a _____ to carry their bag of clubs and to assist them.

14) At the clinic, her baby had an _____ against measles, mumps and rubella.

15) The wingspan of the great _____ is the largest of any bird.

16) _____ are often progenitors in allergies and allergic reactions to certain foods.

17) The athlete's performance reached a _____ and ceased to improve.

18) Two dummy chimneys maintained the building's _____ appearance.

19) Special _____ rates applied for visitors from overseas.

20) The Latinised symbol for the Japanese _____ is ¥.   **Score** | 10

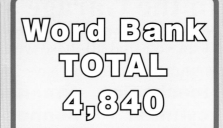

Word Bank TOTAL 4,840

Across

(242)

1. A modern building that is extremely tall.
7. A hill or mountain with a level top.
8. A simple outer garment for the body in the form of a single piece of heavy cloth, often wool, with a slit in it for the head.
10. A covering of hair, or something resembling hair, worn on the head for adornment.
11. Legal or official punishments.
14. A frame or stand with three legs.
16. Sincere and genuine, with no intention to mislead or deceive.
17. A large, long-winged seabird that inhabits cool southern oceans and spends most of its life in flight.

Across (continued)

18. A container for liquid or powder that is loaded into a device.
19. Having both sides of a central dividing line correspond or be identical to each other.

Down

2. A unit of Japanese currency.
3. Food sources that are rich in protein molecules.
4. A very small room, or part of another room, fitted out as a kitchen.
5. Somebody who visits places away from home for pleasure.
6. Somebody in a theatre whose job is to provide the missing words for actors who have forgotten their lines.
8. Little by little.
9. A small box or tin used for storing something, especially tea.
12. A plane figure that has three sides and three angles.
13. The injection of a serum into somebody's body to create immunity to a disease.
15. A series of sessions in which something that is to be done later is practised.

Don't forget to go back to page **18** and complete **Oliver's Mystery Word**.

Mystery Letter [ ]

Score / 20

In the Garage Workshop

Can you find all these words in the picture below? Write the correct word against each number. When you have finished you can colour in the picture if you want to.

mechanic	**spanner**	**wheels**	**jack**	**chain**
cylinder	**bonnet**	**heater**	**hoist**	**toolbox**
battery	**exhaust**	**spark plug**	**axle stand**	**screwdriver**

1._____ 2._____ 3._____

4._____ 5._____ 6._____

7._____ 8._____ 9._____

10._____ 11._____ 12._____

13._____ 14._____ 15._____

36 © 2006 Stephen Curran

In the Butcher's Shop

Can you find all these words in the picture below? Write the correct word against each number.

knives	cash register	mincer	chops	slicer
turkey	pies	joints	scales	pasties
butcher	cleaver	sausages	burgers	saw

1._____   2._____   3._____

4._____   5._____   6._____

7._____   8._____   9._____

10._____   11._____   12._____

13._____   14._____   15._____

© 2006 Stephen Curran

heal
serving
cenotaph
leveret

professional
roulette
glider
skiing

tourniquet
antiseptic
encouragement
ukelele

Across

243

2. A monument erected as a memorial to a dead person or dead people buried elsewhere.
3. To become, or cause to become, shrunken or wrinkled.
5. An agent that prevents or reduces infection.
10. An instrument like a small guitar with four strings.
14. A young hare.
15. Alone.

Across (continued)

17. Support of a kind that inspires confidence and a will to continue.
18. A gambling game with a spinning wheel.
19. The activity, sport or pastime of travelling on skis.

Down

1. Waiting on customers in a shop.
3. A fabric square worn by women over the shoulders, or head and shoulders, or used to wrap a baby in.
4. A tight encircling band applied around an arm or leg in an emergency to stop severe arterial bleeding.
6. A quiver or shudder.
7. A single expansion and contraction of an artery, caused by a beat of the heart.
8. Engaged in an occupation as a paid job rather than as a hobby.
9. An engineless aircraft.
11. Making a long and difficult journey, especially on foot.
12. Judged legally to be unable to pay off personal debts.
13. Suffering from, or carrying, a disease that can be transmitted by direct or indirect contact.
16. To make a person or injury healthy and whole.

Put the mystery letter (✳) into the box marked **243** below. Add in the mystery letters from puzzles **244** to **249** then rearrange them to make **Kate's Mystery Word**. The clue is **BEAUTY**.

243	244	245	246	247	248	249

Mystery Word:

Now rearrange them:

Score

/20

pulse	shrivel	
tremor	unaccompanied	
shawl	trekking	
bankrupt	contagious	

Exercise 243a

1) She usually sings _____ but today she is with a band.

2 He declared himself _____ and removed his burden of debt.

3) The casino welcomes gamblers and has tables for blackjack, _____ and craps.

4) Unless they can _____ the rift in their party, they stand little chance in the election.

5) Impetigo is very _____ : many children in the class will be affected.

6) She booked a series of lessons with the _____ at the golf club.

7) The _____ slipped the tow at 2,000 feet and banked sharply to starboard.

8) The fruit was old and had begun to _____ in the warmth of the room.

9) George Formby strummed the _____ and sang humorous songs.

10) A _____ is born fully furred and with its eyes open.   **Score** [/10]

Exercise 243b

11) The baby was christened wearing the _____ that its mother had worn.

12) They stood on the touchline and shouted _____ to the team.

13) He used his tie as a _____ in a desperate attempt to stop the bleeding.

14) The earthquake's _____ was felt over fifty miles from the epicentre.

15) The nurse cleaned the wound with _____ and applied a dressing.

16) They tried pony _____ for the first time while on holiday in Wales.

17) Their _____ instructor on the piste wore a red sweater and red woollen hat.

18) The Queen laid a wreath of poppies at the _____ on behalf of the nation.

19) The player _____ from the far end is a former Wimbledon champion.

20) The doctor felt her _____ : it was slow and weak.   **Score** [/10]

bachelor   **headgear**   **propeller**
aqualung   **trophy**   **composer**
overturn   **estuary**   **bassoon**
violence   **thrive**   **overcoat**

Across

244

4. Something worn on the head.
6. The remains of an animal or plant preserved from an earlier era inside a rock or other geological deposit.
7. A cup, shield, plaque, medal, or other award given as a token of victory, success, or other achievement.
11. To turn something upside down.
12. Somebody who writes music.
14. An electronic device that accepts, processes, stores and outputs data at high speeds according to programmed instructions.
17. A book, play or film that has an exciting plot involving crime, mystery or espionage.

Across (continued)

18. A Native North American heelless shoe made of deerskin or other soft leather.
19. The sudden loud release of energy and a rapidly expanding volume of gas.
20. To grow vigorously and healthily.

Down

1. An unmarried man.
2. A telephone, or to call somebody on the telephone.
3. The wide lower course of a river where the tide flows in, causing fresh and salt water to mix.
5. The use of physical force to injure somebody or damage something.
8. A heavy coat worn over other outer clothes.
9. A low-pitched double-reed instrument of the oboe family.
10. A revolving shaft with spiral blades that causes a ship or aircraft to move by the backward thrust of water or air.
13. Somebody, especially a king or queen, who rules a state or territory, usually for life and by hereditary right.
15. Somebody whose job is to design buildings and advise on their construction.
16. An underwater breathing apparatus used by divers.

Mystery Letter

Score
20

monarch	architect	
explosion	phone	
fossil	moccasin	
thriller	computer	

Exercise 244a

1) They stood on the stern and watched the wake made by the ship's _____ .

2) Johann Sebastian Bach was a prolific German _____ and organist.

3) She packed a copy of his latest _____ to read on her holiday.

4) He had been a _____ all his life and it was unlikely that he would marry now.

5) She plays _____ in the woodwind section of the philharmonic orchestra.

6) He moved the shrub and it appeared to _____ in its new location.

7) She is a self-made woman and the _____ of her own fortune.

8) They sailed down the river to the _____ , where the tidal race was quite strong.

9) She switched on her laptop _____ and logged on to the internet.

10) He took off his _____ and carried it over his arm.

Score [/10]

Exercise 244b

11) Anti-royalists campaign to replace the _____ with a president.

12) "I now call upon our guest speaker to present the _____ to the winning team."

13) The storm's _____ was extremely destructive, damaging buildings and vehicles.

14) He threaded the lace around the back of the _____ and tied it at the front.

15) She left a voice-mail message asking him to _____ her when he got in.

16) It was a huge _____ that left a pall of thick black smoke over the town.

17) Emile Gagnan and Jacques Cousteau developed the _____ in 1942.

18) Their lawyer asked the Court of Appeal to _____ the verdict.

19) Burning _____ fuels increases carbon dioxide emissions and pollution.

20) Boxers wear protective _____ whilst sparring.

Score [/10]

confetti	offshore	throttle
conker	moonlight	arguable
graph	overcast	contest
untrue	pianist	overhead

Exercise 245a

1) The ship was too late to enter the port so it anchored _____ until the morning.

2) He made a hole through the _____ , then threaded and knotted the string.

3) The library books were _____ and she was fined when she returned them.

4) The rioters built a _____ of burning cars across the street.

5) They awoke to another _____ day with little chance of sunshine.

6) The arrests resulted in the _____ of large amounts of stolen property.

7) The race started: the motorcyclist opened the _____ and raced into the lead.

8) Her paternal grandfather was Polish and her _____ grandfather was Welsh.

9) The great pyramids built by the ancient Egyptians are truly _____ .

10) The Russian spy planned to _____ to the West.   Score ◻ 10

Exercise 245b

11) He measured the _____ of the two concentric circles from their common centre.

12) The scout troop entered a team in the _____ and finished in second place.

13) She returned the high ball with a powerful _____ smash.

14) The ground outside the registry office was littered with colourful _____ .

15) It's _____ whether Andrés Segovia is the father of the modern classical guitar.

16) She collected all the data, then used a computer program to _____ the results.

17) His command of the language is poor and the task of translating is _____ .

18) The concert _____ is a highly acclaimed virtuoso on the keyboard.

19) In the clear night air the _____ reflected off the water's dark surface.

20) He was banished from England for being _____ to the King. Score ◻ 10

Word Bank

Word Bank TOTAL 4,900

overdue
radii
laborious
maternal

defect
recovery
barricade
fabulous

Across

245

3. Straight lines extending from the centre of a circle to its edge.
6. Very cloudy, with no sun showing.
8. Small pieces of coloured paper or dried flowers thrown over the bride and groom at a wedding.
10. Able to be supported or proved with evidence or arguments.
11. Not in accordance with the facts or what is known.
12. A failing, blemish, or flaw.
15. Positioned directly above somebody or something.
17. The gaining back of something lost or taken away.

Across (continued)

18. Requiring a great deal of effort.
19. Amazingly, or almost unbelievably, great or wonderful.

Down

1. Somebody who plays the piano.
2. A barrier that protects defenders or blocks a route.
4. The pale cool light that shines from the Moon on a clear night.
5. On or over land that is near water.
7. To challenge or question something.
9. To kill or injure a person or animal by squeezing the throat.
13. A horse chestnut, without its spiny casing.
14. Belonging or relating to motherhood, a mother, or mothers in general.
15. Late or after the scheduled time, especially in arriving, occurring, or being paid.
16. A diagram used to indicate relationships between two or more variable quantities.

Mystery Letter

Score /20

© 2006 Stephen Curran

43

Word Bank

technical   mysterious   bureau
massive   access   hyperactive
excommunicate   systematic   cab
tedious   devious   nun

Across

246

3. Tending to be beneficial or favourable towards somebody or something.
4. Past participle of *'shine'*.
7. To exclude a baptized Christian from taking part in Communion.
12. Small sweet food items such as chocolate bars, mints and toffee.
13. Boring because of being long, monotonous, or repetitive.
14. Rounded and swollen-looking.
15. Carried out in a methodical and organized manner.
16. Large, solid, and heavy.

Across (continued)

18. Allowing light to pass through with little or no interruption or distortion, so that objects on the other side can be clearly seen.

Down

1. The ability or power to bear prolonged exertion, pain, or hardship.
2. About whom or which little is known or explained.
5. Skilled in practical or scientific subjects.
6. A preposition or adverb indicating the direction, destination or position of somebody or something.
8. The possibility or means of entering or approaching a place.
9. The surround of a fireplace, especially its projecting top.
10. Not straightforward, sincere, and honest in or about your intentions or motives.
11. Abnormally active, restless, and lacking the ability to concentrate for any length of time.
14. A narrow desk with a writing surface and drawers.
17. The part of a large vehicle where the driver or operator sits.
19. A member of a religious community of women.

Mystery Letter ☐

Score ◻ / 20

44

© 2006 Stephen Curran

candy	transparent
friendly	shone
endurance	bulbous
mantelpiece	to

Word Bank TOTAL 4,920

Exercise 246a

1) She put the letters behind the ornament on the _____ .

2) He hailed a horse-drawn _____ and asked the driver to take him to Claridge's.

3) The residents gave the new arrivals a _____ welcome to their street.

4) Rehearsals can be _____ but they should guarantee a fine performance.

5) Experts with _____ expertise were needed to solve the complex problem.

6) He could see the car coming: its headlights _____ brightly through the trees.

7) "May we have some _____ floss when we visit the end of the pier?"

8) He has a red, _____ nose caused by heavy drinking over many years.

9) They went to the _____ de change to purchase some Euro.

10) It is a _____ illness about which little is known.   **Score** ⟋ 10

Exercise 246b

11) The route was _____ : they often thought that they had taken a wrong turn.

12) After he stopped exercising, he gained a _____ amount of weight.

13) She feared the Church would _____ her brother for heresy.

14) Running a marathon severely tested his _____ but he completed the course.

15) They considered the possible causes one at a time, in a _____ way.

16) The novitiate took her final vows and became a _____ , to be known as 'Sister Mary'.

17) His motives are completely _____ and totally selfish.

18) He was _____ and never seemed to tire of running around excitedly.

19) She entered her password to _____ the computer network.

20) "Remember! It is similar _____ and different *from*."   **Score** ⟋ 10

---

formulate	**judo**	**photocopy**
fungus	**carnivorous**	**exhilarate**
literal	**anniversary**	**vigorous**
gymnasium	**conflict**	**grey**

Exercise 247a

1) She made a _____ of the completed form before posting it.

2) The highwayman waited for another opportunity to _____ a traveller.

3) The police officer gave to the court a simple, _____ account of the incident.

4) The _____ was busy and all of the exercise equipment was in use.

5) He took his time to _____ a plan: he could not afford any mistakes.

6) The _____ squirrel has contributed to the decline of the indigenous red squirrel.

7) "He never lacks _____ and is always eager to complete any challenge."

8) She sprinkles _____ onto her soups and salads to add texture and flavour.

9) The rocket's _____ system malfunctioned and it plunged into the sea.

10) One thousand litres of water have about one _____ of mass. **Score** [/ 10]

Exercise 247b

11) The _____ Act of 1940 enabled enemy spies to be prosecuted and executed.

12) Honey _____ grows on living trees and on dead and decaying woody material.

13) He is engrossed by his video game and _____ to everything else.

14) The circulation returned to her hand after minutes of _____ rubbing.

15) A card from the Queen arrived for their golden wedding _____ .

16) *Elaphrosaurus* was a _____ dinosaur of the late Jurassic period.

17) *Judogi* is the name for the traditional costume used for _____ practice and competition.

18) She had to learn complex chemical _____ for her exam.

19) The latest findings _____ with those of the original report.

20) The bold designs _____ the viewer's imagination. **Score** [/ 10]

Word Bank

formulae
oblivious
motivation
waylay

croutons
tonne
guidance
treachery

Across

247

4. Leadership or direction.
8. Extremely strong and active, physically and mentally.
9. A disagreement or clash between ideas, principles, or people.
13. A unit of weight equal to 1,000 kg.
14. Adhering strictly to the basic meaning of an original word or text without further elaboration or interpretation.
17. A copy of something printed, written, or drawn that is produced almost instantly by a photographic process in a machine designed for the purpose.
19. Small pieces of fried bread used as a garnish for soups, salads and other dishes.
20. To draw something up carefully and in detail.

Down

1. Betrayal or deceit.
2. A spore-producing organism such as mildews, moulds, mushrooms, rusts, smuts, and yeast.
3. To lie in wait for somebody.
5. To make somebody feel happy, excited, and more than usually vigorous and alive.
6. A Japanese martial art in which opponents attempt to throw or pin each other, or hold each other in a lock.
7. A feeling of interest or enthusiasm that makes somebody want to do something.
10. Feeding mainly on the flesh of other animals.

Down (continued)

11. A date that is observed on an annual basis because it is the same date as a remarkable event in a past year.
12. Unaware of or paying no attention to somebody or something.
15. A hall equipped for physical exercise or physical training of various kinds.
16. Prescribed and more or less invariable ways of doing something to achieve a particular end.
18. The colour of ash or lead.

Mystery Letter

Score

/ 20

47

Word Bank

exuberance	subordinate	cyclic
hexagonal	psychic	comprehension
gateau	coniferous	vengeance
psychiatrist	cutlery	polo

Across

248

3. Behaviour that shows a lack of respect and shameless boldness.
5. A game played by teams on horseback, with players using long-handled mallets to drive a wooden ball into a goal.
6. Uncertain about an outcome or conclusion.
7. Knives, forks and spoons used for eating.
11. Lower than somebody else in rank or status.
12. A large building in which goods, raw materials, or commodities are stored.
14. An irresistible alluring quality that somebody or something possesses.
16. The grasping of the meaning of something.

Across (continued)

17. A fact or occurrence that can be observed.
18. To behave or think in a socially acceptable or expected way.
19. To make a feature of something more noticeable.

Down

1. A rich cake, usually consisting of several layers held together with a cream filling.
2. Occurring or repeated in cycles.
4. Any tree that has thin leaves (needles) and produces cones.
5. A doctor trained in the treatment of people with mental illnesses.
8. The feeling of being full of happy high spirits and vitality.
9. With six straight sides and six angles.
10. Punishment that is inflicted in return for a wrong.
13. A boat built to operate and travel for long periods underwater.
15. Outside the sphere of scientific knowledge.

Mystery Letter ☐

Score ◻ / 20

warehouse	**phenomenon**	 Word Bank TOTAL 4,960
glamour	**conform**	
accentuate	**impudence**	
dubious	**submarine**	

Exercise 248a

1) The _____ captain scanned the horizon through the periscope.

2) Her uncle gave the couple a beautiful canteen of _____ as a wedding present.

3) He wore a white _____ neck sweater under his jacket to protect him from the cold.

4) "The chocolate _____ looks very rich, so I'll just have a small slice please."

5) Their boisterous behaviour is merely a display of youthful _____ .

6) Each gang sought _____ for the other's violent acts.

7) A _____ test examines a student's understanding of a short text.

8) Ectoplasm is a strange paranormal _____ that many scientists refute.

9) There have been many studies into claims to supernatural _____ powers.

10) " _____ the syllable that has the accent over it." **Score** / **10**

Exercise 248b

11) Education on the risks to health has dissipated the _____ of smoking.

12) Goods that are subject to import duty are placed in a bonded _____ .

13) The soft wood from _____ trees, such as spruce, is ideal for papermaking.

14) "Your _____ is astonishing! I have never known such rudeness."

15) Graphite is a six-sided crystal that crystallizes in the _____ crystal system.

16) _____ form is a technique of musical construction using a recurring theme.

17) All electrical goods must _____ to stringent European safety standards.

18) His doctor referred him to a _____ to treat his neurosis.

19) She authorized a _____ to deputize for her during her absence.

20) The thesis is based on several _____ theories. **Score** / **10**

boycott	firework	exclusion
translucent	feat	denim
recompense	sought	ambitious
divan	capillary	flaw

Exercise 249a

1) The activists asked consumers to _____ the company and its fur products.

2) The organization of food distribution was _____ and many went without.

3) The sides of a meniscus fall due to _____ action within a container.

4) The delicate wings are so _____ they are almost transparent.

5) Success seems unlikely, but nothing is impossible and he remains _____ .

6) In her bedsitter, the _____ is used as a sofa during the day and as a bed by night.

7) The _____ exploded high in the air in a starburst of brilliant colour.

8) Six _____ ships, full of convicted criminals, left Plymouth for Australia.

9) There is a _____ in his argument that can be exploited by his opponents.

10) "He was dressed entirely in _____ : blue from head to toe!"   **Score** ⬜ 10

Exercise 249b

11) He sought _____ for the injuries he sustained in an accident at work.

12) The headache from her _____ was intense: she felt sick and debilitated.

13) They watched the aircraft _____ to the stand where it discharged its passengers.

14) Sir Steve Redgrave achieved a great _____ winning five successive Olympic gold medals.

15) He was threatened with _____ from school if his bad behaviour continued.

16) The baby drank her entire feed: not even a _____ remained in the bottle.

17) "A car like that is an _____ in today's economic climate!"

18) Peter Bird was _____ to be the first to row solo across the Pacific Ocean.

19) He knew she was at home: he could see her _____ on the curtain.

20) As the water rose, they _____ higher ground.   **Score** ⬜ 10

Word Bank

optimistic	taxi
silhouette	migraine
extravagance	chaotic
millilitre	transport

Word Bank TOTAL 4,980

Across

249

1. The act of preventing something or somebody from entering or participating.
5. A unit of volume equal to one thousandth of a litre.
9. Completely disordered and out of control.
12. An outline of somebody or something filled in with black or a dark colour on a light background.
15. An extremely narrow, thin-walled blood vessel.
16. A recurrent, throbbing, very painful headache.
17. Allowing light to pass through, but only diffusely, so that objects on the far side cannot be clearly distinguished.

Across (continued)

18. To pay another for doing work or for performing a service.
19. A remarkable act or achievement involving courage, skill, or strength.

Down

1. Excessive or wasteful spending of money.
2. Tending to take a hopeful and positive view of future outcomes.
3. Having a strong desire to be successful in life.
4. A defect in an object that makes it imperfect or less valuable.
6. Past tense of 'seek'.
7. To cease or refuse to deal with something as a protest against it.
8. A package of manufactured chemicals designed to make a loud and brilliant explosion when lit.
10. A hard-wearing cotton cloth that is typically used to make jeans.
11. A bed with no headboard or footboard.
13. To carry people or goods from one place to another.
14. A car whose driver is paid to transport passengers, typically for short distances.

Don't forget to go back to page **38** and complete **Kate's Mystery Word**.

Mystery Letter

Score

/20

Book Eleven Word List

abbey	capable	cowardly	energy
absence	capillary	create	enormous
accentuate	carnivorous	creation	essay
access	cartridge	creditable	estuary
accommodation	cathedral	crime	evaporate
acquaint	cenotaph	croutons	evidence
acquaintance	challenge	crystal	exceeding
acquainted	chaotic	cuckoo	excitement
acquire	character	cutlery	exclusion
advertise	chess	cyclic	excommunicate
advertisement	Chinese	dainty	execute
albatross	chisel	decision	exhausted
ambition	choir	defect	exhilarate
ambitious	circumstance	definite	explosion
angle	circus	denim	extravagance
angling	civil	deposit	extravagant
anniversary	civilized	description	extreme
annoy	cleanliness	design	extremely
annoyed	coconut	despair	exuberance
antiseptic	college	despise	fabulous
apparent	collie	destination	faithful
application	combination	destitute	famine
approve	commence	destruction	fanatical
aqualung	commit	detail	fatal
architect	complaint	develop	feat
arguable	compliment	devious	filleting
arrival	composer	difference	firework
assassinate	comprehension	digest	flavour
assistance	computer	digestion	flaw
athletic	comrade	disappoint	formulae
authoress	concern	dissolve	formulate
bachelor	conclusion	distribute	fossil
badminton	confetti	divan	fragrant
bankrupt	conflict	division	freight
barricade	conform	domestic	friendly
bassoon	coniferous	dubious	frigid
beverages	conker	elegant	fungus
boycott	consideration	ellipse	gateau
bulbous	contagious	emergency	generous
burden	contest	emigrant	genuine
bureau	continually	emigrate	glamour
cab	conversation	encouragement	glider
caddy	convert	endeavour	granite
candy	convey	endurance	graph

Book Eleven Word List

gratitude	liable	oppose	proclaim
grey	literal	opposite	professional
guarantee	luxury	opposition	programme
guidance	magnificent	oppress	prompter
gymnasium	maintain	optimistic	pronounce
hand-grenade	majestic	origin	propeller
hazardous	manageable	original	proteins
headgear	mantelpiece	overcast	provision
heal	margin	overcoat	provoke
heir	marvellous	overdue	psychiatrist
heroic	massive	overhead	psychic
hexagonal	maternal	overturn	pulse
honourable	medicine	parliament	punctual
hosiery	messenger	patient	pursue
hula-hula	migraine	pattern	pursuit
humiliate	millilitre	peaceable	quaint
humour	mischievous	penalties	quarry
hyperactive	miserable	pension	quench
ideal	moccasin	pentagon	radii
impatience	monarch	phenomenon	rallies
impatient	moonlight	phone	reasonable
impudence	moral	photocopy	reception
impudent	motivation	photograph	recollect
incident	mould	phrase	recommend
independent	mourn	physical	recompense
influence	muscle	pianist	recovery
innocent	mutiny	piecemeal	reference
inoculation	mysterious	pierce	reflect
instruction	national	pilot	rehearsals
insurance	numerous	pirouette	release
intelligence	nun	pistol	reliable
intelligent	objection	plateau	remainder
intention	obliging	polo	remembrance
interfere	oblivious	poncho	reserve
invalid	observatory	portrait	residence
invention	obstinate	poultry	resign
isles	occasion	poverty	response
item	occasionally	practise	reveal
judgment	octagon	presence	roulette
judo	offence	pretence	rumour
kitchenette	offend	principle	sacrifice
laborious	offshore	probable	salute
ladle	operation	probably	sandwich
leveret	opinion	proceed	satisfaction

Book Eleven Word List

scheme	submarine	toiled	ukelele
section	subordinate	tonne	umpire
seize	suitable	torrent	unaccompanied
sensation	supreme	tourist	unaffected
serving	sustain	tourniquet	untrue
shawl	swollen	transform	vacant
shield	symmetrical	translate	vapour
shipping	systematic	translucent	variety
shone	tambourine	transparent	vengeance
shrivel	taxi	transport	ventilation
silhouette	technical	traveller	vigorous
skiing	tedious	treachery	violence
skyscraper	telegram	trekking	volume
society	telegraph	tremor	vulgar
solve	tenant	triangle	waitresses
sought	tennis	trifle	warehouse
soul	thorough	tripod	waylay
source	thriller	trophy	wholly
Spain	thrive	tropics	wig
squirrel	throttle	type	witness
strength	to	typewriter	Yen
strengthen	tobacco	tyrant	yield

Congratulations!

You have now learnt to spell **4,980** words, know what they mean and how to use them in a sentence.

Now move on to **Book 12** to learn lots more words to add to your word bank total.

Exercise 228a

1) conversation
2) photograph
3) intention
4) Telegram
5) phrase
6) principle
7) national
8) choir
9) combination
10) fatal

Exercise 228b

11) ventilation
12) telegraph
13) Cathedral
14) domestic
15) physical
16) punctual
17) section
18) consideration
19) continually
20) sensation

Exercise 229a

1) heroic
2) majestic
3) seize
4) pilot
5) miserable
6) tropics
7) tyrant
8) item
9) extravagant
10) pistol

Exercise 229b

11) circumstance
12) assistance
13) remembrance
14) vacant
15) elegant
16) athletic
17) insurance
18) tenant
19) ideal
20) fragrant

Exercise 230a

1) probable
2) influence
3) description
4) cleanliness
5) witness
6) angle
7) convert
8) probably
9) destruction
10) reasonable

Exercise 230b

11) liable
12) energy
13) concern
14) trifle
15) reliable
16) despair
17) muscle
18) capable
19) despise
20) convey

Crossword No. 228

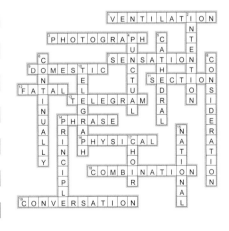

Crossword No. 229

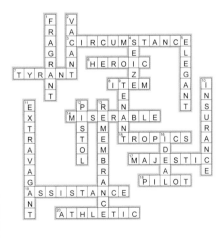

Crossword No. 230

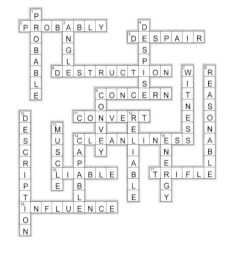

Letter = S

Letter = C

Letter = B

Answers

Exercise 231a
1) Circus
2) absence
3) definite
4) ambition
5) genuine
6) presence
7) crime
8) reference
9) pretence
10) umpire

Exercise 231b
11) instruction
12) granite
13) objection
14) reception
15) evidence
16) salute
17) residence
18) medicine
19) famine
20) satisfaction

Exercise 232a
1) disappoint
2) swollen
3) abbey
4) acquaint
5) detail
6) distribute
7) burden
8) acquaintance
9) execute
10) strength

Exercise 232b
11) gratitude
12) acquainted
13) develop
14) deposit
15) destitute
16) pattern
17) luxury
18) strengthen
19) acquire
20) volume

Exercise 233a
1) application
2) reveal
3) approve
4) oppose
5) traveller
6) College
7) opposition
8) messenger
9) offend
10) response

Exercise 233b
11) flavour
12) design
13) reflect
14) remainder
15) opposite
16) release
17) oppress
18) challenge
19) reserve
20) resign

Crossword No. 231

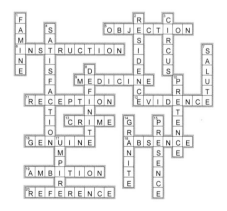

Letter = N

Crossword No. 232

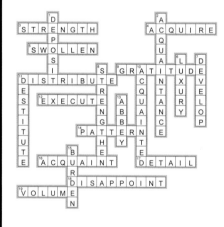

Letter = E

Crossword No. 233

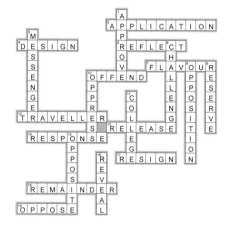

Letter = A

Answers

Exercise 234a

1) advertisement
2) occasionally
3) invalid
4) independent
5) vapour
6) yield
7) enormous
8) pierce
9) generous
10) practise

Exercise 234b

11) rumour
12) excitement
13) impudent
14) innocent
15) mischievous
16) shield
17) numerous
18) marvellous
19) advertise
20) occasion

Exercise 235a

1) invention
2) heir
3) mould
4) frigid
5) proclaim
6) operation
7) patient
8) provoke
9) civil
10) poultry

Exercise 235b

11) digest
12) impatience
13) pronounce
14) civilized
15) proceed
16) impatient
17) commit
18) opinion
19) digestion
20) soul

Exercise 236a

1) tobacco
2) complaint
3) dissolve
4) solve
5) shipping
6) division
7) endeavour
8) annoy
9) decision
10) poverty

Exercise 236b

11) pension
12) recommend
13) recollect
14) annoyed
15) wholly
16) comrade
17) conclusion
18) humour
19) commence
20) provision

Crossword No. 234

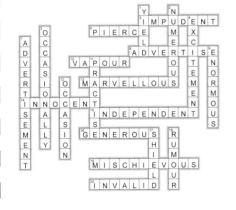

Letter = O

Crossword No. 235

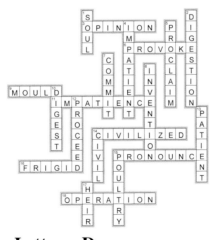

Letter = D

Crossword No. 236

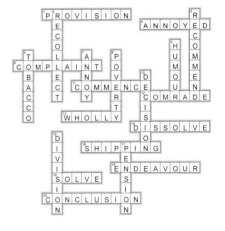

Letter = P

At the Birthday Party

1. SLICE	2. BALLOONS	3. PATCH	4. DONKEY	5. LEMONADE
6. JELLY	7. PRESENTS	8. FAIRY CAKE	9. CARD	10. ZIP FASTENER
11. DOLL	12. CANDLES	13. ECLAIR	14. BLINDFOLD	15. ENTERTAINER

On the Canal

1. LOCK	2. RAILING	3. BAIT	4. LANDING NET	5. BOW
6. PAINTER	7. LIFEBELT	8. FENDER	9. REEL	10. STERN
11. FISHING ROD	12. DUCK	13. NARROWBOAT	14. LOCK KEEPER	15. HAMPER

Answers

Exercise 237a

1) transform
2) quench
3) margin
4) sandwich
5) mutiny
6) Spain
7) variety
8) quaint
9) programme
10) original

Exercise 237b

11) translate
12) dainty
13) arrival
14) character
15) society
16) create
17) sacrifice
18) origin
19) crystal
20) moral

Exercise 238a

1) emigrate
2) manageable
3) extremely
4) creditable
5) pursuit
6) intelligent
7) Chinese
8) supreme
9) obstinate
10) suitable

Exercise 238b

11) mourn
12) peaceable
13) extreme
14) pursue
15) scheme
16) creation
17) interfere
18) honourable
19) emigrant
20) source

Oliver's Page of Knowledge

1. Joseph Foljambe
   Plough.
2. Laszio Biro
   Ballpoint Pen.
3. Charles Babbage
   Computer.
4. Gustaf Erik Pasch
   Safety Match.
5. Frank Whittle
   Jet Engine.
6. James Hargreaves
   Spinning Jenny.
7. Trevor Bayliss
   Clockwork Radio.
8. Robert William Thomson
   Pneumatic Tyre.
9. Rudolph Diesel
   Diesel Engine.
10. John Logie Baird
    Television.

Crossword No. 237

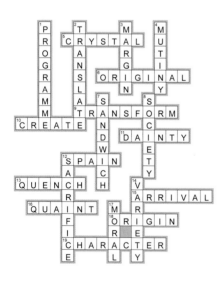

Letter = H

Crossword No. 238

Letter = O

Answers

Exercise 239a

1) judgment
2) magnificent
3) squirrel
4) typewriter
5) sustain
6) intelligence
7) quarry
8) compliment
9) Parliament
10) maintain

Exercise 239b

11) torrent
12) essay
13) apparent
14) vulgar
15) incident
16) portrait
17) offence
18) type
19) difference
20) thorough

Exercise 240a

1) exhausted
2) angling
3) destination
4) hand-grenade
5) badminton
6) authoress
7) chisel
8) ellipse
9) isles
10) filleting

Exercise 240b

11) evaporate
12) faithful
13) cuckoo
14) hosiery
15) guarantee
16) accommodation
17) hazardous
18) freight
19) cowardly
20) humiliate

Exercise 241a

1) beverages
2) Pentagon
3) pirouette
4) waitresses
5) hula-hula
6) obliging
7) Observatory
8) tambourine
9) exceeding
10) toiled

Exercise 241b

11) ladle
12) coconut
13) fanatical
14) rallies
15) tennis
16) Chess
17) assassinate
18) emergency
19) octagon
20) collie

Crossword No. 239

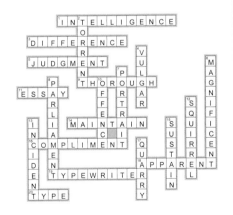

Letter = J

Crossword No. 240

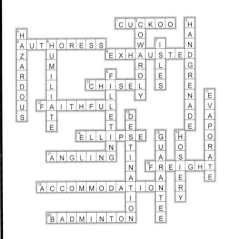

Letter = R

Crossword No. 241

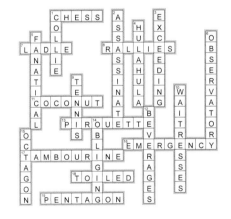

Letter = S

In the Garage Workshop

1. HOIST	2. MECHANIC	3. SCREWDRIVER	4. EXHAUST	5. TOOLBOX
6. SPANNER	7. HEATER	8. BATTERY	9. BONNET	10. CHAIN
11. CYLINDER	12. SPARK PLUG	13. JACK	14. AXLE STAND	15. WHEELS

In the Butcher's Shop

1. TURKEY	2. JOINTS	3. SAUSAGES	4. SAW	5. PASTIES
6. SLICER	7. CASH REGISTER	8. SCALES	9. BUTCHER	10. MINCER
11. CHOPS	12. BURGERS	13. PIES	14. KNIVES	15. CLEAVER

Answers

Exercise 242a

1) rehearsals
2) kitchenette
3) skyscraper
4) piecemeal
5) prompter
6) Triangle
7) penalties
8) unaffected
9) wig
10) cartridge

Exercise 242b

11) poncho
12) tripod
13) caddy
14) inoculation
15) albatross
16) Proteins
17) plateau
18) symmetrical
19) tourist
20) Yen

Exercise 243a

1) unaccompanied
2) bankrupt
3) roulette
4) heal
5) contagious
6) professional
7) glider
8) shrivel
9) ukelele
10) leveret

Exercise 243b

11) shawl
12) encouragement
13) tourniquet
14) tremor
15) antiseptic
16) trekking
17) skiing
18) Cenotaph
19) serving
20) pulse

Exercise 244a

1) propeller
2) composer
3) thriller
4) bachelor
5) bassoon
6) thrive
7) architect
8) estuary
9) computer
10) overcoat

Exercise 244b

11) monarch
12) trophy
13) violence
14) moccasin
15) phone
16) explosion
17) aqualung
18) overturn
19) fossil
20) headgear

Crossword No. 242

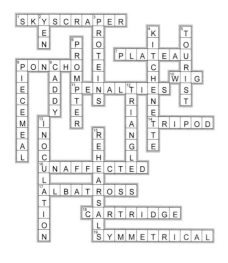

Letter = U

Crossword No. 243

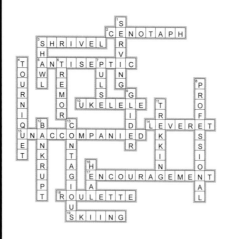

Letter = P

Crossword No. 244

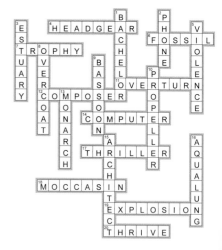

Letter = M

Answers

Exercise 245a
1) offshore
2) conker
3) overdue
4) barricade
5) overcast
6) recovery
7) throttle
8) maternal
9) fabulous
10) defect

Exercise 245b
11) radii
12) contest
13) overhead
14) confetti
15) arguable
16) graph
17) laborious
18) pianist
19) moonlight
20) untrue

Exercise 246a
1) mantelpiece
2) cab
3) friendly
4) tedious
5) technical
6) shone
7) candy
8) bulbous
9) bureau
10) mysterious

Exercise 246b
11) devious
12) massive
13) excommunicate
14) endurance
15) systematic
16) nun
17) transparent
18) hyperactive
19) access
20) to

Exercise 247a
1) photocopy
2) waylay
3) literal
4) gymnasium
5) formulate
6) grey
7) motivation
8) croutons
9) guidance
10) tonne

Exercise 247b
11) Treachery
12) fungus
13) oblivious
14) vigorous
15) anniversary
16) carnivorous
17) judo
18) formulae
19) conflict
20) exhilarate

Crossword No. 245

Letter = T

Crossword No. 246

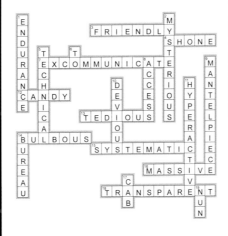

Letter = O

Crossword No. 247

Letter = A

Answers

Exercise 248a

1) submarine
2) cutlery
3) polo
4) gateau
5) exuberance
6) vengeance
7) comprehension
8) phenomenon
9) psychic
10) Accentuate

Exercise 248b

11) glamour
12) warehouse
13) coniferous
14) impudence
15) hexagonal
16) Cyclic
17) conform
18) psychiatrist
19) subordinate
20) dubious

Exercise 249a

1) boycott
2) chaotic
3) capillary
4) translucent
5) optimistic
6) divan
7) firework
8) transport
9) flaw
10) denim

Exercise 249b

11) recompense
12) migraine
13) taxi
14) feat
15) exclusion
16) millilitre
17) extravagance
18) ambitious
19) silhouette
20) sought

Crossword No. 248

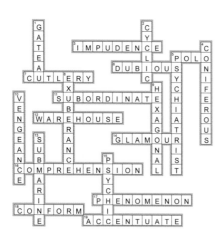

Crossword No. 249

Letter = C

Letter = C

Mystery Word

S C B N E A O

B E A C O N S

Mystery Word

D P H O J R S U

J O D H P U R S

Mystery Word

P M T O A C C

C O M P A C T

PROGRESS CHARTS

Scores

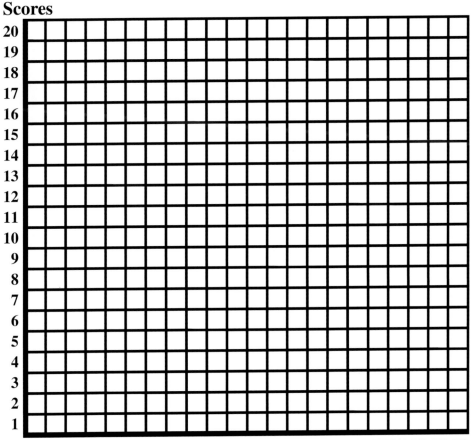

228 229 230 231 232 233 234 235 236 237 238 239 240 241 242 243 244 245 246 247 248 249

Exercises

Shade in your score for each exercise on the graph. Add them up for your total score out of 460. Ask an adult to work out the percentage.

Total Score

Percentage

 % **A**

Scores

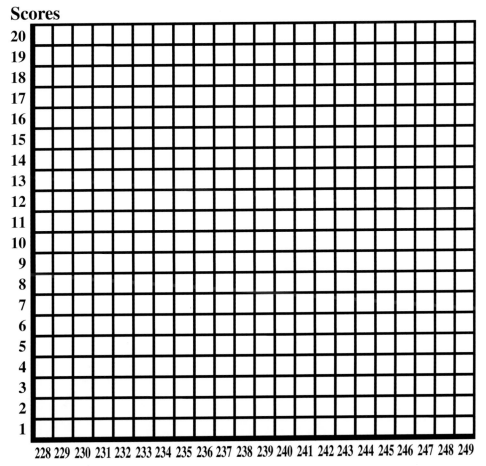

228 229 230 231 232 233 234 235 236 237 238 239 240 241 242 243 244 245 246 247 248 249

Crosswords

Shade in your score for each crossword on the graph. Add them up for your total score out of 460.

Total Score

Percentage

 % **B**

For the average percentage add %A and %B and divide by 2

Overall Percentage

%

CERTIFICATE OF

ACHIEVEMENT

This certifies

_____

has successfully completed

11+ Spelling & Vocabulary

WORKBOOK **11**

Overall percentage
score achieved

%

Comment _____

_____

Signed _____

(teacher/parent/guardian)

Date _____